CARLOS TRILLO
Writer

EDUARDO RISSO
Artist

Red Moon

THE KINGDOM OF NEVER

SAF
COMICS

Carlos Trillo • Eduardo Risso
RED MOON
Volume #3: The Kingdom of Never

© Strip Art Features, 2005. All rights reserved.

Editorial office:
SAF COMICS
Krpanova 1, 3000 Celje, Slovenia
Tel. (386-3) 425-0500
Fax: (386-3) 545-1774

www.safcomics.com
info@safcomics.com

First edition: November 2005
ISBN: 90-77001-85-9

Printed in Slovenia by SAF - Tiskarna Koper

EVERYONE IS SO CONTENT.

WELL, EVERY-ONE...

... BUT ME.

ANTOLIN HAS GONE AWAY.

BY HIMSELF.

AND I DIDN'T EVEN BOTHER TO GO ALONG AND HELP LOOK FOR CROCKER AND THEO.

SHOULD I FOLLOW HIM TO NEVER?

OR SHOULD I STAY HERE WITH MY FATHER, NOW THAT I'VE RESCUED HIM?

WHO CAN GIVE ME AN ANSWER?

WHO?

I WILL ANSWER YOUR QUESTION, MOON.

BUT... IT'S THE STAR WHO'S TALKING TO ME...

... AND HER VOICE IS THE SAME AS MY MOTHER'S.

I *AM* YOUR MOTHER, SILLY.

1

4

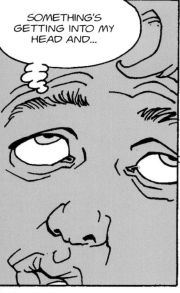

SOMETHING'S GETTING INTO MY HEAD AND...

... I THINK I'M GOING TO PASS...

... OUT...

WHAT'S WRONG WITH OUR MASTER?

THUMP

HE MUST HAVE DRANK TOO MUCH!

OF COURSE. HE DRANK A TOAST TO ALL OF HIS SUBJECTS. HA, HA!

NOW THAT HE'S PASSED OUT...

... I'LL MAKE HIM DREAM ABOUT ME.

LISTEN UP, DEAR HUSBAND...

?

TYL, MY LOVE!

YOU DON'T NEED TO WORRY ABOUT OUR DAUGHTER.

SHE WENT TO HELP HER FRIEND ANTOLIN.

OH, NO! I'LL GO LOOK FOR HER RIGHT AWAY!

3

PUFF.

AND I THOUGHT MOON WAS MY FRIEND...

... BUT NO, SHE DIDN'T EVEN BOTHER COMING ALONG.

I LOST MY VOICE SCREAMING ANTOLIN'S NAME.

I THINK I'D BETTER FIND SHELTER OR I'M GONNA FREEZE TO DEATH.

THERE'S A CAVE.

I'LL REST HERE AND WAIT FOR THE STORM TO END.

IT'S DARK AS HELL IN HERE.

HEY, YOU TWO...

BE CAREFUL. A LITTLE FURTHER UP IS THE BORDER BETWEEN BURIEN AND NEVER.

DON'T WORRY, SIR! WE'RE AWARE OF THAT.

WHAT KIND OF HAIR LOTION DO YOU USE?

HAIR LOTION?

WE DON'T USE ANY.

THE LOCALS HAVE REALLY STRANGE HAIRDOS...

WELL, DON'T SAY LATER THAT NO ONE WARNED YOU.

EXCUSE ME, SIR, MA'AM. MAY I ASK YOU SOMETHING? IT'S KIND OF PERSONAL.

BUT IF YOU KEEP WALKING ABOUT ONE THOUSAND YARDS AHEAD, YOU'LL SEE WHY.

GOOD-BYE.

I DON'T UNDERSTAND. SEE WHAT? HOW TO GET SUCH HAIRSTYLES?

MOON, I THINK THAT...

... THIS IS WHERE BURIEN ENDS AND NEVER BEGINS.

12

WHAT SHALL WE DO?

WELL... WE HAVE TO JUMP...

ON THREE. ONE, TWO...

... THREE!

IT'S NOT SO BAD HERE, IS IT?

ON THE CONTRARY. IT'S GREAT! INSTEAD OF THAT FREEZING COLD, IT'S NICE AND HOT.

RATHER UNPLEASANT HEAT, THOUGH, I'D SAY.

WELL... YES. NOW THAT I TOOK MY SHOES OFF...

... THE GROUND IS BURNING. I CAN BARELY WALK ON IT!

OUCH!

SORRY, ANTOLIN. THAT WAS THE ONLY WAY TO PREVENT ME FROM GETTING HORRIBLE BLISTERS.

IF WE DON'T DO SOMETHING SOON...

... WE COULD DEHYDRATE AND BURN TO DEATH IN THE HOT SUN.

WE SHOULD AT LEAST COVER OUR HEADS.

HATS! HATS!

11

13

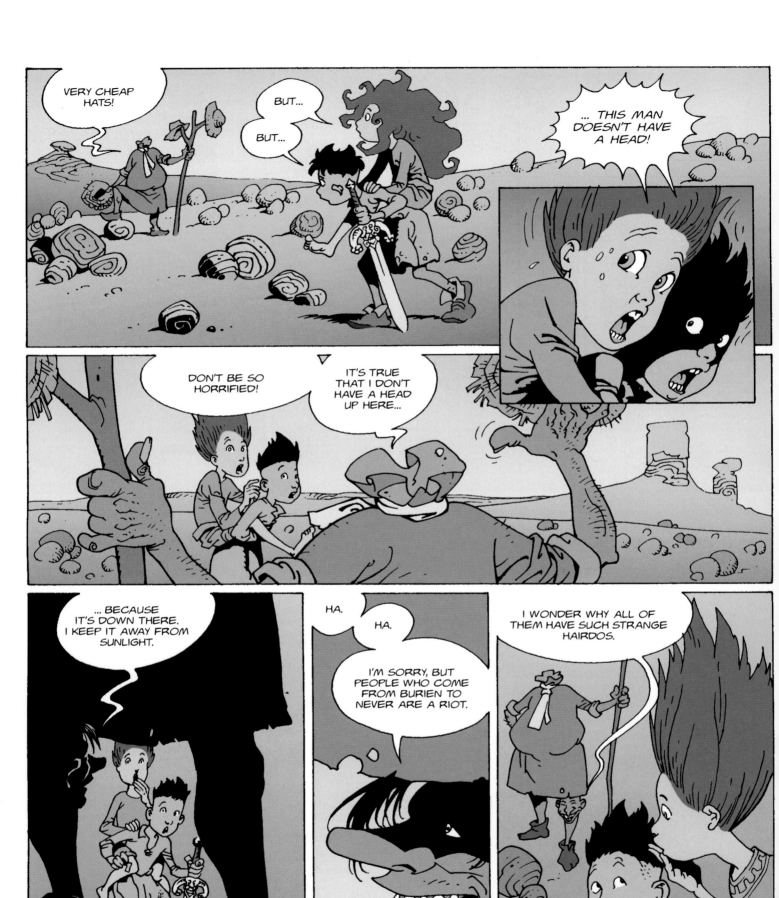

14

15

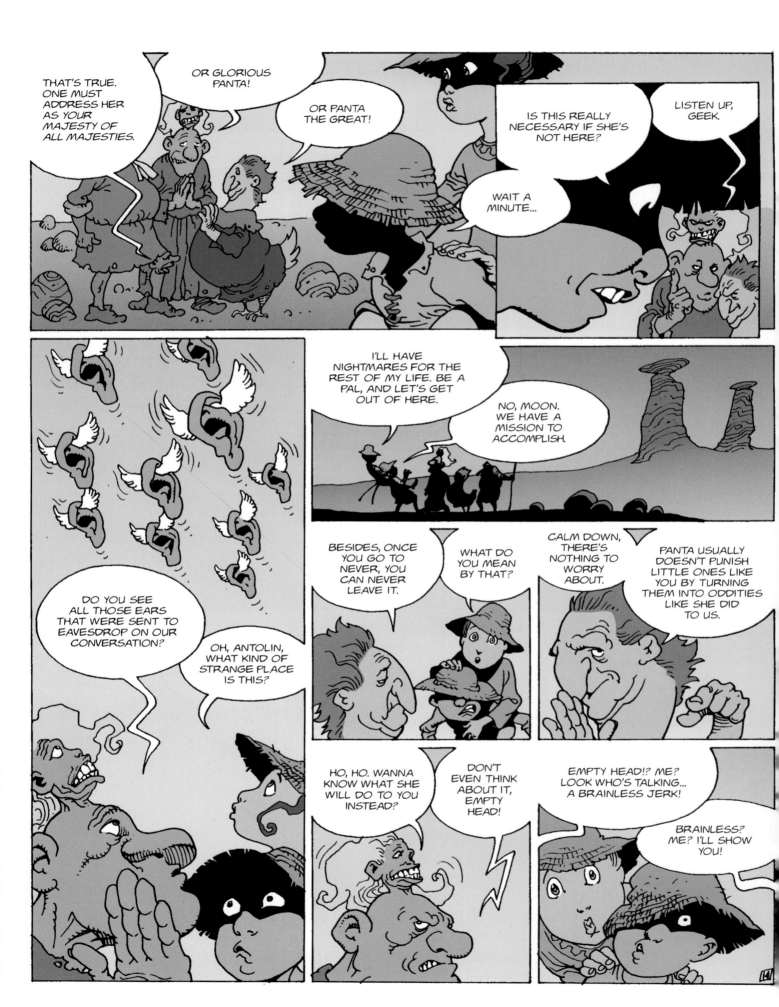

16

THE TWO COMEDIANS FROM THE LEAGUE... ONE SHORT AND CHUBBY, THE OTHER A THIN BALD GUY?

YES! HAVE YOU SEEN THEM?

ME? NO, NEVER.

HEY, MR. GURG!

WHY ARE WE GOING THROUGH THIS CAVE?

IT'S A SHORTCUT.

ON THE OTHER SIDE OF THE MOUNTAIN IS PANTA'S CASTLE.

GOOD THING I DIDN'T TELL THEM WHAT PANTA USUALLY DOES TO CHILDREN.

YES. THEY WERE RELIEVED WHEN THEY LEARNED THAT PANTA WASN'T GONNA TURN THEM INTO CREATURES LIKE US.

OF COURSE. WHY MAKE THEM WORRY?

HOW WOULD THEY FEEL NOW IF THEY KNEW THAT PANTA EATS CHILDREN?

19

IS SOMETHING WRONG, GURG?

N-N-NO, IT'S JUST... THAT...

... A ROCK FROM THE CEILING FELL DOWN... AND HIT ME ON THE HEAD.

LOOK, ANTOLIN!

QUITE PECULIAR ANIMALS LIVE HERE IN NEVER!

YES, BUT WHAT I REALLY FIND CURIOUS IS...

... THAT GURG TOLD US PANTA'S CASTLE WAS ON THIS SIDE OF THE MOUNTAIN BUT I DON'T SEE ANYTHING.

THAT'S NOT SO STRANGE. IT LIKES TO WALK AROUND. IT'LL BE BACK IN A JIFFY.

WHO LIKES TO WALK AROUND? THE CASTLE?

YES. THAT'S WHAT I SAID.

BUT YOU WON'T HAVE TO WAIT MUCH LONGER. HERE IT COMES.

OH.

KREK

20

I WANNA GET OUT OF HERE.

WAIT, CHILDREN. YOU'LL NEVER FIND A BETTER ACCOMMODATION...

... THAN THIS LUXURIOUS COMFORTABLE PALACE, WHICH BELONGS TO OUR SOVEREIGN, PANTA!

BESIDES, YOU WON'T HAVE TO CLIMB TO REACH THE DOOR.

SEE? THE DOOR IS COMING TO YOU.

... IT'S OPENING.

STEP INSIDE. BIG PANTA IS EXPECTING YOU.

GO ON, GO ON!

WILL PANTA TELL US WHERE MY FRIENDS, THEO AND CROCKER, ARE?

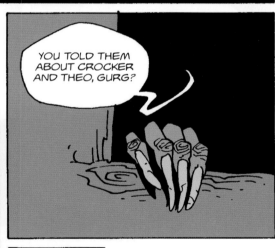

YOU TOLD THEM ABOUT CROCKER AND THEO, GURG?

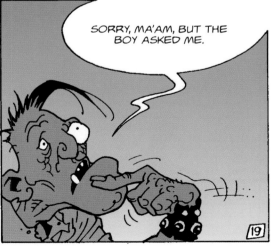

SORRY, MA'AM, BUT THE BOY ASKED ME.

BUT I DIDN'T TELL THEM EVERYTHING, YOUR MAJESTY.

YOU REALLY CAN'T KEEP YOUR MOUTH SHUT, GURG.

CROAC!

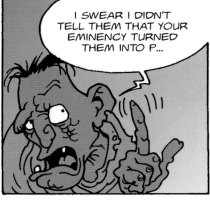

I SWEAR I DIDN'T TELL THEM THAT YOUR EMINENCY TURNED THEM INTO P...

WILL YOU SHUT UP!

ZAP!

I'D LIKE YOU TO FINISH WHAT GURG WAS ABOUT TO SAY, MIGHTY LADY.

YOU TURNED THEM INTO P...? P.... WHAT?

CROAC!

P...

P...

PI PI PI PI!

I TURNED THEM INTO FAMOUS MUSICIANS.

YES.

SO NOW, NOT ONLY ARE THEY SKILLFUL CIRCUS PERFORMERS, BUT THEY CAN ALSO PLAY THE TRUMPET AND LUTE.

DO COME IN, PLEASE.

IT'S ALMOST DINNERTIME.

20

WHAT SHOULD WE DO?

WELL, A DINNER INVITATION SOUNDS TEMPT-ING. AND I'M HUNGRY, TOO.

SO... MAYBE...

THE DOOR SLAMMED!

I'M SURE IT'S DUE TO THE DRAFT.

IT LOOKS LIKE...

LIKE...

... LIKE IT WON'T BE SO EASY TO LEAVE THIS PLACE.

WHAT WAS THAT NOISE?

THAT WAS MY... TEETH. THEY STARTED DANCING WITHOUT MY PERMISSION.

WHY ARE YOU WHISPERING? WHAT'S THE BIG SECRET?

OH...

... IT'S...

... UH...

... WE WERE ONLY SAYING THAT...

BUBON? WHO'S THAT?

MY LITTLE SON!

OH!

THEY TOOK HIM AWAY FROM ME WHILE I WAS DIGGING OUT THE EYE OF A CYCLOPS-SNAKE!

HE WAS IN HIS RED BASKET PLAYING WITH A HOOF NECKLACE...

... AND ALL OF A SUDDEN HE WAS GONE.

OH, MY.

OH MY, WHAT?

WHEN I WAS A CHILD, CROCKER AND THEO FOUND ME IN A RED BASKET WITH A HOOF NECKLACE BETWEEN MY HANDS.

HMMM.

DO YOU PERHAPS KNOW WHAT BUBON WAS WEARING ON HIS FEET?

SLIPPERS!

WHO TOLD YOU THAT, STUPID KID?

NO ONE, MA'AM. I WAS WEARING SLIPPERS WHEN CROCKER AND THEO FOUND ME.

YOU WERE?

I DON'T LIKE THIS CONVERSATION, NOT ONE BIT.

24

HMM, LET ME ASK YOU ONE MORE QUESTION.

WHAT DID YOU USUALLY DO WITH YOUR THUMB WHEN YOU WERE A CHILD?

ERR... WELL I...

I USED TO SUCK IT!

BUBON USED TO SUCK IT, TOO!

AND HE HAD BLACK HAIR LIKE YOU AND HIS EYES WERE THE SA...

SNIFF?

OH, NO.

MY SAUCE IS BURNING!

A... ANTO... GULP... ANTOLIN...

IS THERE THE SLIGHTEST CHANCE THAT YOU'RE A SON OF THAT... THING?

DON'T BE RIDICULOUS, MOON.

I'M JUST HUMORING HER SO SHE WILL LET US GO.

THANK GOODNESS.

IT'S DONE. I PUT THE FIRE OUT.

... MY SON!

GURG! WHERE ARE YOU, GURG?

CROC CROAC

WHAT ARE YOU DOING DISGUISED AS A TOAD? RETURN TO YOUR NORMAL LOOK...

... NOW!

ARGH.

THAT RAY WAS KINDA STRONG.

DON'T WASTE MY TIME WITH SILLY REMARKS.

I HAVE AN ANNOUNCEMENT TO MAKE. AND IT'S HUGE.

CALL ALL MY SUBJECTS!

YES, YOUR EXCELLENCY...

... RIGHT AWAY.

EK!

IT'S PANTA.

SHE WANTS TO TELL US SOMETHING!

COME ON, LET'S GO!

QUICKLY!

SHE DOESN'T LIKE TO WAIT!

EVERYONE'S COMING. THEY'LL BE HERE IN NO TIME.

THANK YOU, MY FAITHFUL GURG.

BECAUSE THERE SEEM TO BE TOO MANY COINCI-DENCES

WELL... I...

... GULP...

ARE YOU SURE YOU'RE JUST HUMORING HER, ANTOLIN?

... I THINK I'M GETTING SCARED.

SILENCE!

COULD I HAVE YOUR ATTENTION PLEASE? THE QUEEN OF NEVER IS GOING TO SPEAK NOW!

BELOVED PEOPLE OF NEVER!

OUCH! WHY IS SHE ALWAYS WEARING TACKED SOLES?

THIS ANNOUNCE-MENT WON'T TAKE LONG.

I HAVE FOUND MY LOST SON!

HIS NAME IS BUBON, AND HE'LL INHERIT EVERYTHING I POSSESS...

... EVERYTHING! AND THIS MEANS YOUR LIVES, YOUR SOULS, YOUR EYES, YOUR MULES...

... BECAUSE ONE DAY HE'LL BECOME THE ALL-MIGHTY KING OF NEVER.

IN OTHER WORDS, WHEN PANTA KICKS THE BUCKET, WE'LL HAVE TO PUT UP WITH HER SON!

I HEARD YOU, MALICIOUS CREATURE. THIS IS FOR YOU!

A COCKROACH! DISGUSTING!

28

30

I'LL SQUASH IT!

NOOO!

DON'T DO IT, LADY. IT'S A POOR LITTLE CREATURE.

ACTUALLY, THIS ISN'T A COCKROACH. THIS IS A BEWITCHED HUMAN.

BESIDES...

... EVEN IF IT WAS A BUG, WHY WOULD YOU KILL IT?

WHOA! WHAT WAS THAT?

YOUR MAJESTY, ARE YOU SURE THAT THIS BOY IS YOUR SON?

JUDGING FROM WHAT I'VE SEEN, HE DOESN'T HAVE BLOODTHIRSTY AND FIERCE INSTINCTS LIKE YOU.

SHHH! SHUT UP, WILL YOU?

DON'T YOU REALIZE, GOSSIP, THAT SHE'LL TURN US ALL INTO FISHES AFRAID OF WATER OR EVEN SOMETHING WORSE?

I'M NOT SAYING THIS TO OFFEND YOU, BELOVED QUEEN, IT'S JUST THAT...

... YOU WOULD HAVE NEVER SAVED THAT REPULSIVE BUG'S LIFE, WOULD YOU?

31

AHEM...

... MY DEAR...

... MY DEAREST MOTHER, YOU...

... YOU DIDN'T RAISE ME. I WAS BROUGHT UP BY THOSE TWO COMEDIANS... THEY'RE POOR BUT HAVE A GOOD HEART.

AHEM.

SO?

MANY TIMES I FELT THAT WHAT THEY TAUGHT ME TOTALLY OPPOSED MY TRUE NATURE.

BUT...

... BUT I THOUGHT THEY BROUGHT ME UP WELL AND...

... OH...!

THEN WHAT?

THEN WHAT?

THEN WHAT?

THEN WHAT?

... AND THEN I TURNED OUT TO BE A GOOD PERSON.

GGGHHH! GOOD! THIS IS REALLY DISGUSTING. I'M GONNA PUKE!

YOU'LL HAVE TO FORGIVE HIM, YOUR MAJESTY.

YES! FORGIVE HIM!

I'M SURE HE'LL LEARN HOW TO BE A BAD BOY.

WITH YOU DIRECTING HIM HE'LL BECOME AN AUTHORITY IN MAKING US SUFFER, JUST LIKE YOU, PANTA.

YOU'RE SO BRIGHT, MY QUEEN, AND YOU'LL TURN HIM INTO A GOO...

... I MEAN BAD BOY.

WELL, MAYBE I SHOULD PUT HIM TO ANOTHER TEST AND...

... GIVE HIM ONE MORE CHANCE.

31

THIS TIME, BE CONVINCING.

TELL ME SOMETHING, SON...

YES, MOM?

DO YOU STILL WANT TO FIND CROCKER AND THEO?

OF COURSE NOT.

GOOD THING, BECAUSE WHEN I TOLD YOU THAT I TURNED THEM INTO FAMOUS MUSICIANS I LIED.

ACTUALLY, I TURNED THEM INTO PIGS, AND I SOLD THEM TO A HAM FACTORY OWNER.

NO!

TELL ME YOU DIDN'T, FILTHY WITCH!

OH! YOU DARE ATTACK ME?

TAKE THIS TRANQUILIZER.

SEE HOW EFFECTIVE IT IS? YOU'VE SHUT UP ALREADY.

AND YOU'RE RATHER STIFF.

TOC

TOC

32

?

NO!

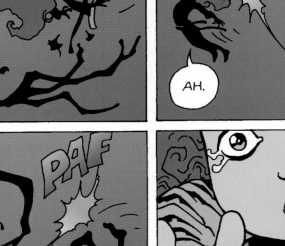

PLAF!

AH.

PAF

UH.

AND SHE'S BACK.

SAVE ME THIS SNACK FOR LATER, CAGE!

SO MANY CONTRADICTORY HOPES...

... HAVE MADE ME LOSE MY APPETITE.

SIGH.

WHAT A MESS.

AND ON TOP OF EVERYTHING, THERE'S THIS SHITTY LOCK THAT HOLDS THE CAGE...

GRRRR.

IF I TRY TO UNLOCK IT WITH THIS HAIRPIN, I'M SURE IT'LL EAT IT.

ARF!

GRRRR.

PLic

UH.

IT WON'T BE EASY TO GET OUT OF HERE.

POOR ANTOLIN...

IS HE ALIVE?

FRANKLY, I DON'T THINK HE IS. PUFF, PUFF.

DON'T SAY THAT, COCKROACH. THAT SCARES ME.

PUFF... PUFF...

AND IT'S ALL YOUR FAULT.

WE WOULD HAVE NEVER GOTTEN INTO THIS TROUBLE, IF MY FRIEND HADN'T TRIED TO SAVE YOUR ASS, GEEK.

SHUT UP AND HEL... PUFF... GH...

... GHHHHH...

... HELP ME WITH THIS BOTTLE. IT WEIGHS LIKE A MILLION TONS.

WHAT'S INSIDE?

SLEEPING POWDER. PANTA TAKES IT EVERY NIGHT.

SHE'S AN INSOMNIAC.

SHE MUST SUFFER FROM SOME SICKNESS THAT GIVES HER HEADACHES AND MAKES HER SLEEPLESS.

WHY DID YOU BRING THIS TO ME?

DIP WHAT REMAINS OF YOUR HAIRPIN INTO THE LIQUID.

AND THEN?

DO I REALLY HAVE TO TELL YOU EVERYTHING?

PUT IT IN THAT PADLOCK'S MOUTH!

GROURGH.

PLIC

RONF!

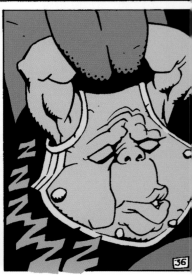

36

38

NOW YOU CAN GET OUT, GIRL.

THANK YOU, ROACH.

BUT WHERE'S PANTA?

SHE MADE HERSELF SOME LIZARD TEA, SEE?

SHE ALWAYS READS SOME BORING BOOKS WHILE SIPPING HER CUP OF TEA.

POUR THE CONTENTS OF THE FLASK IN HER TEA BEFORE SHE RETURNS FROM THE LIBRARY!

YES, OF COURSE.

HURRY UP! SHE'S COMING!

GLB GLB GLB

SPELLS AND CHARMS

SNIFF.

41

PANTA IS SLEEPING LIKE A LOG. LET'S USE THIS OPPORTUNITY TO GET OUT OF HERE. ALL OF US.

BE CAREFUL. TRY NOT TO BREAK MY POOR FRIEND.

DON'T WORRY. WE'LL GET HIM OUT OF HERE, AND WE ALSO KNOW HOW TO TURN HIM HUMAN AGAIN.

HELP ME PULL THE TRUCK! COME ON, ALL OF YOU!

YES.

OF COURSE.

EXCUSE ME, BUT...

... I THINK I'LL BE MORE USEFUL IF I BRING THIS BOOK WITH ME INSTEAD OF PULLING THE TRUCK.

SPELLS AND CHARMS

HE'S ALWAYS AVOIDING HIS DUTIES.

THAT'S NOT FAIR!

WELL, PANTA COULD WAKE UP AT ANY MOMENT.

... AND START HUNTING US DOWN...

... AND BEWITCH US INTO SOMETHING EVEN WORSE THAN WE ARE NOW.

MAYBE SOME OF YOU WOULD LOVE TO TURN INTO DANDRUFF?

WE DECIDED TO HELP THIS LITTLE GIRL, AND MAYBE SHE'LL HELP US GET RID OF THIS PRESUMPTUOUS SHREW, RIGHT?

YES, BUT WHAT DOES THAT BORING BOOK HAVE TO DO WITH ALL THIS?

OF COURSE NOT. YOU THINK THIS BOOK CAN HELP US?

OH, YES!

BECAUSE IT SAYS IN HERE HOW TO FIGHT AND PREVAIL AGAINST PANTA, IDIOTS!

DON'T YOU SEE THE BOOK'S TITLE? "SPELLS AND CHARMS"!

BUNCH OF MORONS.

AHEM!

FRANKLY, I DON'T UNDERSTAND WHAT'S GOT INTO ME.

A-HA.

AHAHA.

THAT PATHETIC RED-HAIRED GIRL TOOK MY STATUE AND DISAP-PEARED!

AND I'M SURE THAT SOME OF MY MISERABLE SUBJECTS MUST HAVE HELPED HER!

BUT THEY WON'T GET FAR!

GUUURG

I'M HERE, MILADY.

I NEED A HORSE. AND I NEED IT NOW, GURG!

THERE ARE NO HORSES IN NEVER, YOUR EXCELLENCY.

THERE AREN'T?

43

45

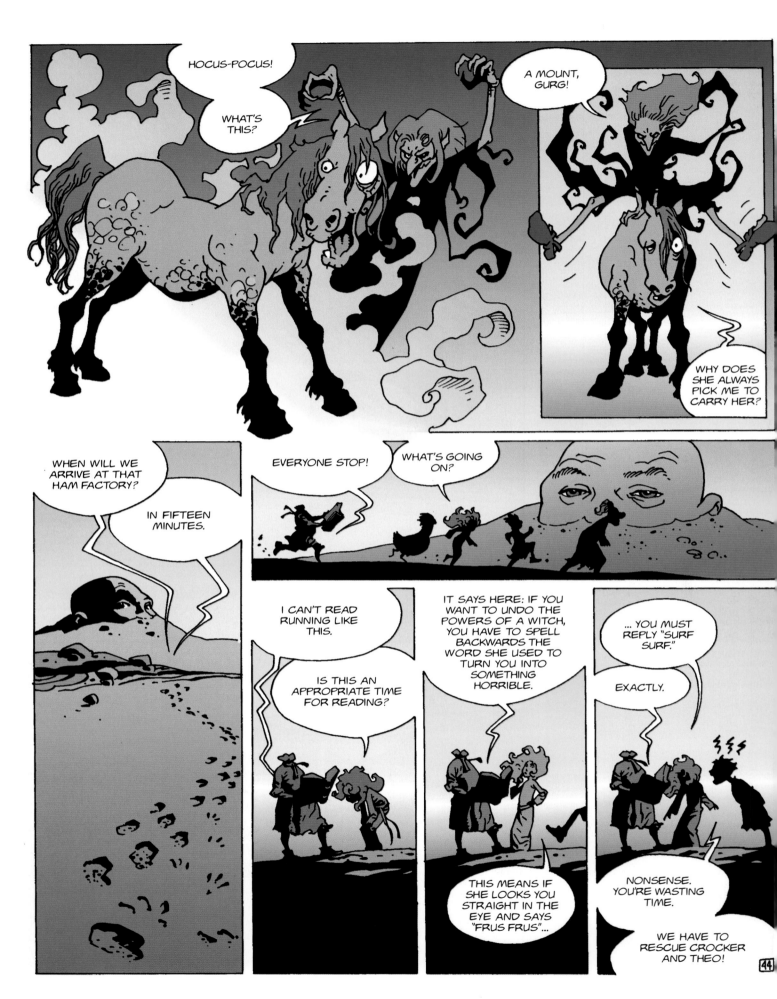

46

48

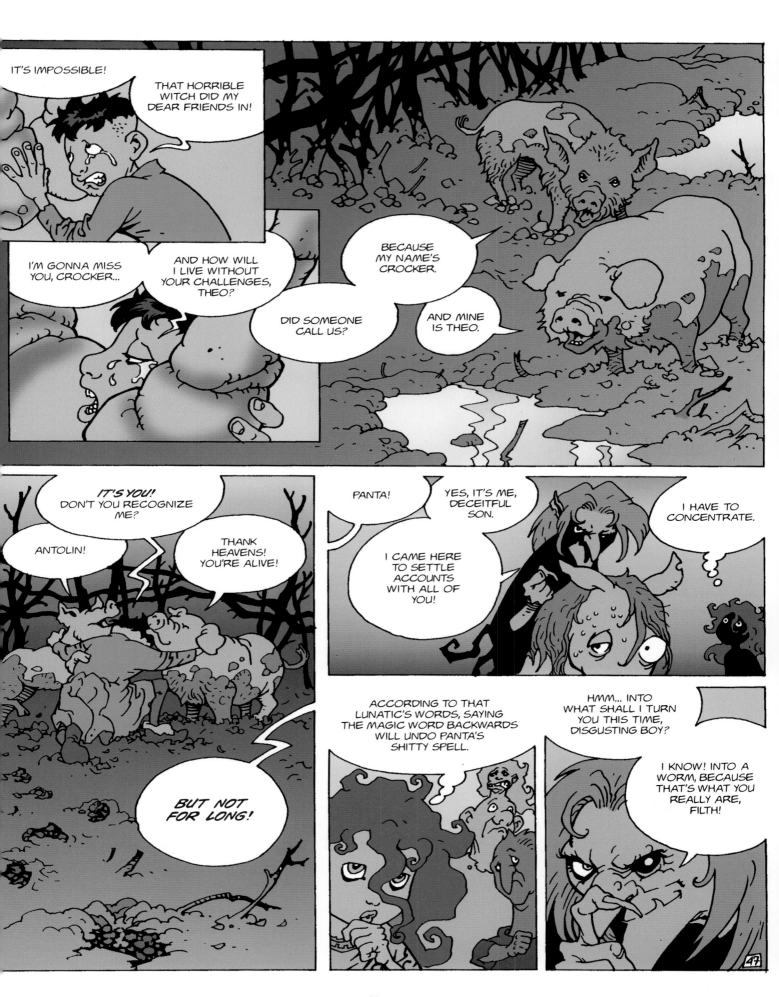

49

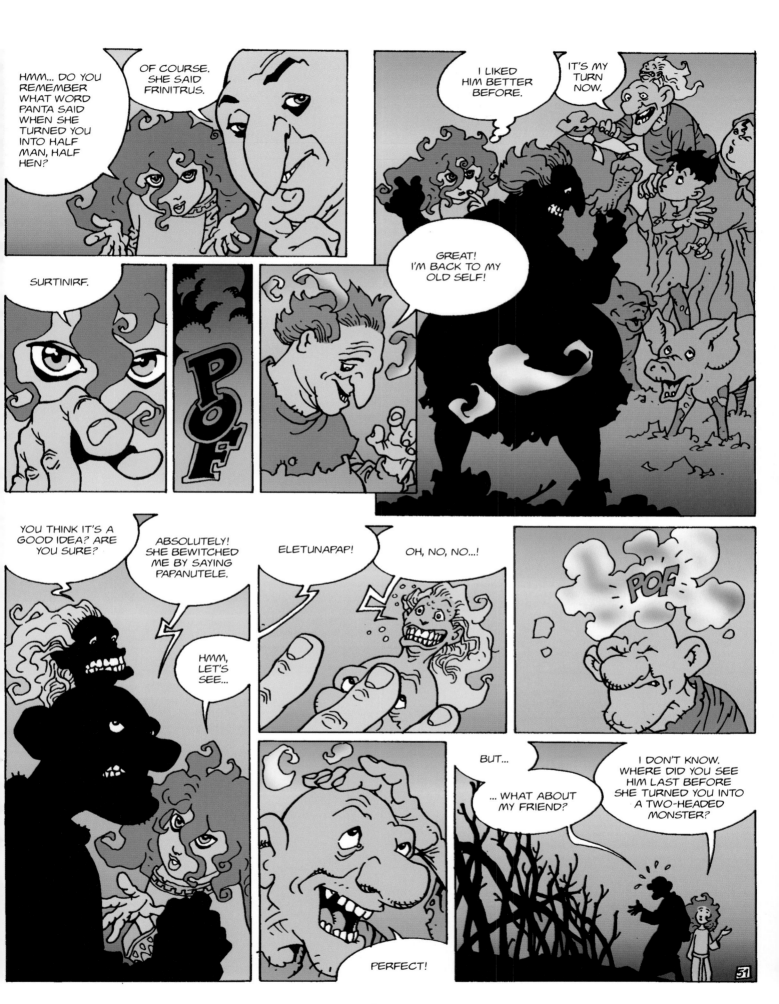

53

YOU'RE COMING ALONG, AREN'T YOU?

HMM, I DON'T KNOW.

WE HAVE TO MAKE OUR OWN WAY. THERE ARE MANY VILLAGES WHOSE INHABITANTS ANXIOUSLY WAIT TO ADMIRE OUR SKILLS.

OF COURSE, ANTOLIN AND WE OWE IT TO OUR AUDIENCE AND...

LOOK...

... WHEN MY DAD SEES THAT WE'RE BACK, HE'LL INVITE EVERYBODY TO A DINNER THAT WILL LAST ONE MONTH AT LEAST.

DIN...

ONE MONTH OF EATING?

COME ON! I DON'T WANNA MAKE MY POOR FATHER WORRY ABOUT HIS DAUGHTER ANY LONGER!

END OF BOOK #3